BIBLE 406
HOW CAN I KNOW GOD EXISTS?

CONTENTS

Author: **Dolores Stedman**
Editor-in-Chief: Richard W. Wheeler, M.A.Ed.
Editor: Janet Monseu
Consulting Editor: John L. Booth, Th.D.
Revision Editor: Alan Christopherson, M.S.

ALPHA OMEGA
PUBLICATIONS

300 North McKemy Avenue, Chandler, Arizona 85226-2618

HOW CAN I KNOW GOD EXISTS?

Who has seen the wind?
  Neither I nor you;
But where the leaves hang trembling,
  The wind is passing thro'.
Who has seen the wind?
  Neither you nor I;
But when the trees bow down their heads,
  The wind is passing by.

 Christina Rossetti

Who has ever seen God?
  Neither I nor you;
But there are things about us,
  That tell us God is true.
Who has ever seen God?
  Neither you nor I;
But when in prayer we bow our heads,
  God will not pass by.

 Dolores Stedman

How do you know the wind exists? You do not need to see the wind to know that it exists. Even though you cannot see the wind, you can see things move. You can feel the wind on your face. You know the wind exists because of what it does.

How can you know that God exists? You cannot see God, either. You can know God lives by the things He does.

In this LIFEPAC you will learn some ways in which you can know that God exists because of the things He has done. You will learn about God's plan for His people. God's plan included His Son coming to earth. You also will learn about a man called Thomas Aquinas who helped show man that God exists. You will study some facts of science in the Bible. Finally, you will study why you need God and the ways that you can know God.

OBJECTIVES

Read these objectives. The objectives tell you what you should be able to do when you have successfully completed this LIFEPAC.

When you have finished this LIFEPAC, you should be able
1. To tell about the beginning of the Jewish nation,
2. To describe how God came to earth,
3. To tell two facts about Thomas Aquinas,
4. To give three facts about science found in the Bible,

5. To explain why man needs God,
6. To tell how man can know God, and
7. To recite four Bible verses.

VOCABULARY

Study these new words. Learning the meanings of these words is a good study habit and will improve your understanding of this LIFEPAC.

argument (är´ gyu munt). A giving of reasons for or against something.

artificial (är tu fish´ ul). Made by human skill or work, not natural.

Canaan (kā´ nun). The land of promise.

craftsman (krafts´ mun). A skilled workman.

create (krē āt´). To make or form; to bring into being.

element (el´ u munt). One of the simple materials from which all other things are made.

exist (eg zist´). To be real.

explosion (ek splō´ zhun). A noisy blowing up of something.

friar (frī´ ur). Member of a religious group.

galaxy (gal´ uk sē). A group of stars.

ignore (ig nôr´). To pay no attention.

Isaac (ī´ zuk). Abraham's son.

poverty (pov´ ur tē). Being poor.

religion (ri lij´ un). Man's beliefs about God.

theory (thē´ ur ē). An idea which explains something people do not understand.

Thomas Aquinas (tom´ us uh kwī´ nus). A religious thinker and teacher.

universe (yü´ nu vėrs´). All created things; everything.

worship (wėr´ ship). Prayer, praise, and honor given to a god.

Note: All vocabulary words in this LIFEPAC appear in **boldface** print the first time they are used. If you are unsure of the meaning when you are reading, study the definitions given.

Pronunciation Key: hat, āge, cãre, fär; let, ēqual, tėrm; it, īce; hot, ōpen, ôrder; oil; out; cup, pùt, rüle; child; long; thin; /TH/ for then; /zh/ for measure; /u/ represents /a/ in about, /e/ in taken, /i/ in pencil, /o/ in lemon, and /u/ in circus.

I. GOD'S PLAN FOR PEOPLE

Remember the story of Adam and Eve. They were God's friends, but they disobeyed God. Satan had tempted them to do a terrible thing. God still loved Adam and Eve very much even though He had to punish them. God loves all people very much even though they have hurt Him by their sins.

God had a plan to help the people on earth. God worked out His plan through the Jewish nation. In this section you will learn about God's plan.

☐ **Review these objectives.**
1.   To tell about the beginning of the Jewish nation, and
2.   To describe how God came to earth.

☐ **Restudy these words.**
Canaan   ignore
exist   Isaac

  Read Genesis, Chapters 12, 13, and 15.

THE JEWISH PEOPLE

Long ago in the land of Ur lived a man named Abram. The people around him prayed to gods made of wood and stone. God told Abram to get away from these people and to move to another country.

Abram took his wife Sarai and moved to a distant land. He had never been in that land before, but he believed God would take care of him.

The promises. After the long, hard trip, God led Abram and his family to a land called **Canaan**.

"I will give all this land to you," God promised Abram. "It will belong to you and to your children forever. I will be your God, and you will be my people."

God said He would give Abram many children and grandchildren and great-grandchildren. God said He would make of him a great nation.

When Abram was out under the night sky, God told him to look up at the stars. God asked Abram to count the stars. Abram could not count the stars because there were so many. Then God told him, "You will have so many children they will be like those stars—too many to count!"

God also said, "People will try to hurt your family. I will punish those who hurt them."

God's promise to Abram has come true. Abram's family has become the Jewish nation, God's special people.

Abraham tried to count the stars.

The family. God gave Abram a new name, Abraham, which means "the father of a great nation." He gave Sarai a new name too. Her new name was Sarah, which means "princess." Abraham and Sarah were the first of God's special people.

Abraham and Sarah had a child whose name was **Isaac**. Isaac had a child, and his name was Jacob. Jacob had twelve sons. The twelve sons of Jacob had children. Their children had children. For hundreds of years, children were born until the number of Jews were thousands and thousands.

Often the Jews were treated very cruelly by other people. God promised them that someday He would give them a Saviour. After hundred of years went by, many of the Jews forgot about the promise.

Most of the Jews lived in sin and **ignored** God's commandments. They did not act like God's special people.

Put the sentences in the correct order by numbering the boxes in each set.

1.1
☐ God gave Abram many children and grandchildren.
☐ God told Abram and Sarai to leave Ur.
☐ God said, "This land will belong to you and to your children."
☐ God led them to a land called Canaan.

1.2
☐ God said, "I will punish those who hurt your family."
☐ God told Abram, "You will have so many children, they will be like the stars—too many to count."
☐ God gave Abram and Sarai new names.
☐ Abraham and Sarah had a child named Isaac.

Fill in this chart.

My name was		My name is
1.3	God changed my name. My new name means "Father of a great nation."	
1.4	The new name God gave me means "Princess."	

Write the correct word in each sentence to tell what God promised.

God   Saviour   people   Canaan
hurt   children   Isaac

1.5 God promised Abraham many _____ .
1.6 God promised the Jewish people a _____ .
1.7 God promised to punish those who _____ the Jewish people.
1.8 God promised, "I will be your a. _____ , and you will by my b. _____ ."
1.9 God promised to give the Jewish people the land of
_____ .

5

Read Matthew 1:18 through 25.

THE JEWISH SAVIOUR

Once a little boy was watching some ants running around on the ground. He thought to himself, "If I wanted to talk to those ants, how would I do it? If I shouted at them, they would not hear me or understand me. I could send them a letter, but they probably would not read it." Then he thought, "If I could become an ant myself, then I could speak to them and they would understand."

God decided to send His Son to earth. He decided to make a body like ours for His Son. Jesus became one of us so that He could tell us about God's love.

Jesus left heaven. While Jesus was in heaven, He made the world. He made Adam and Eve. He watched Adam and Eve disobey and sin. They had to be judged, but God loved them and sent Jesus to die for them. He also loves us. Jesus came to earth to die for our sins, too.

How much Jesus loved us to be willing to leave heaven and to be born as a baby. How much He must have loved us to die for our sins!

Do you see God's plan? Jesus is the Jewish Saviour! God had promised Him to the Jews hundreds of years ago.

Jesus came to earth. Jesus came and was born into a Jewish family, but He had **existed** with His Father in heaven since the beginning of time. He had always been in heaven with God because He is God.

Mary was Jesus' mother, but her husband, Joseph, was *not* Jesus' Father. Jesus did not need an earthly father. God was Jesus' Father.

Today Jesus is in heaven getting a place ready for us.

Complete this activity.

1.10 Try to imagine what it was like for Jesus to leave a wonderful place like heaven and come down to earth. How do you feel about Jesus' doing that for you? Write Jesus a note telling Him how you feel.

Dear Jesus,

_____

_____

_____

_____

_____

_____

_____

_____

Love,

_____

Teacher check _____

Initial   Date

Write the correct answer.

1.11   Who was Jesus' Father? _____

1.12   Where was Jesus before He came to earth as a baby? _____
_____

Connect the matching numerals with a line.

1.13   Jesus came to earth to

2   3   4 ———————

———————

2   3   4 ——————— -

1.14   Jesus died for our

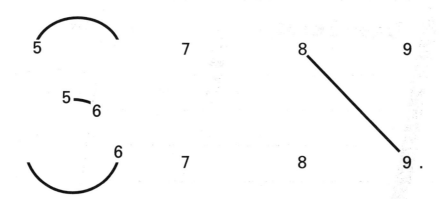

 **Complete this activity.** Unscramble and rearrange the letters to find the name of the land God gave Abraham. Write the word on the line below.

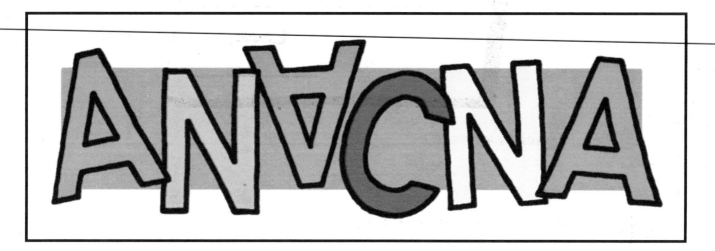

1.15   _____

 Complete this puzzle.
Take the first letter of the word ANSWER,
The second letter from the word ABOUT,
The third letter from the word STRAIGHT,
Find the fourth letter in the word SARAH,
The fifth letter in the word SOUTH,
Find the sixth letter in the word MOUNTAIN, and
The seventh letter in the word EXCITEMENT.

1.16   Who am I? _____

Underline the homonyms in these sentences.
Homonyms are words that sound alike.

1.17 God used to speak aloud and tell the leaders what they were allowed to do.

1.18 Do not walk in the woods in bare feet. You may see a bear and have to run.

1.19 The whole class saw the hole in the fence.

1.20 We bought a sail for the boat at the boat sale.

1.21 Do you see the dew on the grass?

Draw a line under the syllable with the schwa sound.

In some words a vowel has a sound somewhat like a short *u* sound, but the sound is weaker. This sound is called the *schwa* sound. The schwa vowel sound is often heard in unaccented syllables. Say each of the following words.

1.22   a lone

1.23   sci ence

1.24   eas i ly

1.25   gal lop

1.26   e qual

Write the words from 1.22 and 1.26 in the following sentences.

1.27 If you study well, you can do your work _____ .

1.28 Jesus _____ is the Saviour for sins.

1.29 Mother will divide the cake into _____ pieces.

1.30 In school the children study _____ .

1.31 The horse moved along the road with a steady _____ .

Review the material in this section to prepare for the Self Test. The Self Test will check your understanding of this section. Any items you miss on this test will show you what areas you need to restudy.

SELF TEST 1

Match these items (each answer, 3 points).

1.01	_____ Abraham	a.	God's special people
1.02	_____ Adam and Eve	b.	princess
1.03	_____ Sarah	c.	a garden
1.04	_____ Isaac	d.	Jewish Saviour
1.05	_____ Canaan	e.	Jesus' home
1.06	_____ Jesus	f.	land of promise
1.07	_____ God	g.	father of a great nation
1.08	_____ heaven	h.	Jesus' Father
1.09	_____ Jewish people	i.	Abraham's son
		j.	tempted by Satan

Put the sentences in the correct order by numbering the boxes in each set (each correct set, 5 points).

1.010

☐ God led them to a land called Canaan.
☐ God said, "This land will belong to you and to your children."
☐ God told Abram to leave Ur.

1.011

☐ God promised Abram many children.
☐ God gave Abram and Sarai new names.
☐ Abraham and Sarah had a child named Isaac.

Use the following words to complete the sentences (each answer, 3 points).

children	God	heaven	hurt
Jesus	people	Saviour	sins

1.012   God promised Abraham many _____ .

1.013   God said, "I will be your God and you will be my _____ ."

1.014   Jesus came to earth to die for our _____ .

1.015   Jesus' Father is _____ .

1.016   Before Jesus came to earth, He was in _____ .

1.017   God promised the Jewish people a _____ .
1.018   God promised to punish those who _____ the
         Jewish people.

Answer *yes* **or** *no* (each answer, 2 points).
1.019 _____ Did the Jews always obey God?
1.020 _____ Do we always obey God?
1.021 _____ Do we deserve to be punished by God?
1.022 _____ Does Jesus love you?
1.023 _____ Did Jesus take our punishment for sin?
1.024 _____ Is Jesus the Saviour from sin?
1.025 _____ Does God keep his promises?
1.026 _____ Can we see the wind?
1.027 _____ Do we know that wind exists?
1.028 _____ Can we see God?
1.029 _____ Do we know that God exists?

Answer these questions (each numbered answer, 5 points).
1.030   If we can't see the wind, how do we know that it is there?

         _____

         _____

1.031   If we can't see God, how do we know He exists? _____

         _____

         _____

1.032   Why did Jesus come to earth? _____

         _____

         _____

1.033   What were two promises God gave to Abram?
         a. _____

         _____

         b. _____

         _____

II. MAN'S SEARCH FOR GOD

Two friends named Mike and Jeff were walking along the beach in the wet sand. Mike said, "I do not believe that we can ever know for sure how the world was made. I think things just happened."

Just then they came to a sand castle. "Oh look," said Mike, "someone has made a sand castle."

"Oh?" said Jeff. "How do you know someone made it? Maybe it just happened."

"Well, don't be silly," Mike exclaimed, "somebody must have made it. It could not just happen."

Jeff stopped, looked at his friend, and asked, "If you cannot believe this sand castle just happened, why do you believe that the world just happened?"

In this section you will learn about **Thomas Aquinas** and his laws to prove that God exists. Of course we know that no one has to prove that God exists. We must accept God on faith.

You will also study about three things God made: the **universe**, the earth, and the human body.

☐ **Review these objectives.**

3. To tell two facts about Thomas Aquinas and
4. To give three facts about science found in the Bible.

☐ **Restudy these words.**

argument	explosion	religion
artificial	friar	theory
craftsman	galaxy	Thomas Aquinas
create	poverty	universe
element		

 Read James 3:13 through 17.

THOMAS AQUINAS AND HIS LAWS

Thomas Aquinas lived hundreds of years ago (1225-1274). He loved to think about deep truths. He often thought about God. During his life he wrote laws to prove that God exists. Thomas was born into an important family in Italy.

Thomas was a large, strong boy. He had big eyes with much understanding in them. He also had a head full of good sense. Thomas loved to study. As a teen-ager he mastered many of the sciences.

He often left his brothers to their warlike playing and joined the adults. Thomas listened to their wise talk. Sometimes he would sit in a corner away from the rest of his family and just think. On stormy nights, as he laid in bed and listened to the thunder, he would ask himself questions about God.

His father wanted Thomas to be a soldier when he grew up. Although Thomas had a good strong body, he did not want to become a soldier. He wanted to work and to study for the church.

"Father," said Thomas, "I wish to be a **friar**."

"A what? A ragged, barefooted friar?"

"Yes, Father."

"And take the vows of **poverty**? And go hungry? Impossible!"

After trying many things to stop him, his family let him go. Thomas put bread, cheese, and fruit into a bundle and set out over the dusty road to school.

His fellow students did not seem to understand him, either. Thomas sat quietly for hours listening and took no part in the talking. Because he was so big and so quiet, they called him "the dumb ox."

One of Thomas's teachers said to the class, "You call Thomas a dumb ox, but I tell you someday the whole world will listen to him."

At the age of thirty-three, Thomas

Thomas became a friar.

Aquinas became a teacher of **religion**. He often prayed, "Lord, help me to understand your power."

He wrote many great things. His laws, or **arguments**, to prove that God exists are well known.

Aquinas's laws say that a first maker or mover in the world who is perfect must exist. A first cause, a last end of all things, and a reason for the **universe** must also exist. Do these laws sound like they describe God?

 Write *true* **or** *false*.

2.1 _____ When he was a boy, Thomas Aquinas loved to sit and think.

2.2 _____ Because he was a big strong boy, his father wanted him to be a soldier.

2.3 _____ Thomas became a soldier.

2.4 _____ Thomas wanted to work and to study for the church.

2.5 _____ When he was a student, Thomas talked a lot about God to others.

2.6 _____ Thomas Aquinas wanted to be rich.

2.7 _____ Today many people read Thomas Aquinas's writings about God.

2.8 _____ The world just happened.

 Complete this activity. When a prefix is placed in front of a word, the prefix changes the meaning of the word. Study the following list of prefixes and their meanings.

Prefix	Meaning
ex-	out of, off, from
im-	in, not
con-	against
com-	with
ad-	to

Read each sentence and write the letter and the word that best completes it.

2.9 Abraham did not _____ about leaving Ur.
   a. complain   b. plain

2.10 Going to Canaan was a/an _____ for Sarah and Abraham.
   a. venture   b. adventure

2.11 Sarah and Abraham were _____ in Canaan.
   a. content (happy)   b. tent

2.12 Obeying God is _____ .
   a. port   b. important

Circle the words that tell about God.

powerful	perfect	destroyer
forgetful	helpless	needed
maker		

2.13   Write the words you circled on this line. Write commas between each word.

God is _____.

Read Colossians 1:12 through 17 and Jeremiah 32:17.

SCIENCE AND THE BIBLE

The Bible is not a science book, but when the Bible talks about things of science, it has been proved to be correct. Not once has the Bible been found to be wrong.

The universe. Can you think about how great the universe is? Did you know that the sun is more than a million times bigger than our earth? The nearest star is about twenty-four trillion miles away (add 12 zeros after 24). About 200 billion stars are in our **galaxy** (add 9 zeros after 200). More than 10,000 galaxies are all moving through space at great speeds. None of these huge stars or planets bump into each other or get on the wrong path. Everything in space moves in an orderly way.

"How did our universe all begin?" This question has been asked by many people. Scientists have tried hard to explain the beginning of the universe. None of their ideas, or **theories** have been accepted by all people.

Some think the universe began with an **explosion** that set the stars and planets in motion. Others think the sun threw off pieces that became stars and planets. Still others think that millions of years ago a tiny thing too small to see suddenly became alive and began to grow. Many men think that the universe just happened.

The Bible tells us very simply that God made these things. God **created** this great universe. He is watching over it right now.

 **Answer** *true* **or** *false*.

2.14 _____ The Bible is a science book.
2.15 _____ Sometimes the Bible is wrong.
2.16 _____ Everything in space moves in an orderly way.
2.17 _____ Many men think the universe just happened.

 Complete this activity.

2.18 Tell about two ways scientists think the universe began.

a. _____

_____

b. _____

_____

 Write the correct answer in the blank.

2.19 The _____ tells us that God made the universe.

2.20 Remember when Abraham tried to count the stars? No wonder he could not do it. In our galaxy alone _____ _____ stars probably exist.

Read Psalm 8.

The earth. Look anywhere and see signs of God. Look at the countless blades of grass and the millions of snowflakes. Each one is a bit different from the others.

Notice the birds that fly and the fish that swim. Each one is made in a special way. Flowers, insects, and animals all prove that God exists. If you were to try to list all of the things God has done and made, you would never get done. The earth is filled with God's works.

The Bible has much information about our earth. At one time some people believed the earth was flat. Isaiah said (Isaiah 40:22) that the earth was round.

Job wrote (Job 38:16) about the "springs of the sea." This fact has been discovered by scientists living today.

BIBLE

4 0 6

LIFEPAC TEST

80 / 100

Name _____

Date _____

Score _____

BIBLE 406: LIFEPAC TEST

Match these items (each answer, 3 points).

1. _____ Isaac
2. _____ friar
3. _____ Abraham
4. _____ God
5. _____ Canaan
6. _____ Jesus
7. _____ Thomas Aquinas
8. _____ Sarai

a. wrote laws to prove God exists
b. member of a religious group
c. Sarah
d. Saviour
e. father of a nation
f. Jesus' Father
g. Abraham's son
h. land of promise
i. Ur

Write the letter of the correct answer in the blank (each answer, 3 points).

9. Life is in the _____ .
   a. blood   c. heart
   b. brain

10. The greatest wonder of all that God created is the _____ .
    a. earth   c. ocean
    b. body

11. Thomas Aquinas wrote laws to prove God _____ .
    a. cares   c. exists
    b. loves

12. All men have a deep need to _____ .
    a. drive a car   c. know God
    b. have a pet

13. The father of the Jewish nation is _____ .
    a. Abraham   c. Isaac
    b. Adam

14. Before Jesus came to earth, He was _____ .
    a. in heaven   c. in Canaan
    b. in Bethlehem

15.　　Jesus came to earth to save people from their _____ .
　　　　a. worries　　　　　　　　　　c. friends
　　　　b. sins
16.　　God gave Abraham and his children the land of _____ .
　　　　a. Ur　　　　　　　　　　　　c. Bethlehem
　　　　b. Canaan

Answer *true* **or** *false* (each answer, 2 points).
17. _____ People deserve to be punished for their sins.
18. _____ Jesus died for our sins.
19. _____ Abraham left Canaan and went to Ur.
20. _____ We know that God exists because of what He does.
21. _____ Joseph was Jesus' real father.
22. _____ You cannot see God, but you can see what He does.
23. _____ God will punish those who hurt the Jews.
24. _____ All religions believe in the true God.

Write the correct word in the blank (each answer, 4 points).
25.　　Jesus was in _____ before He came to earth.
26.　　The Bible writers were told what to write by _____ .
27.　　God promised the Jewish people a _____ .
28.　　God speaks to us through the _____ .

Complete the following Bible verses (each answer, 5 points).
29.　　Psalm 100:3, "Know ye that the Lord _____
　　　　_____
　　　　_____ ."
30.　　Psalm 139:14, "I will praise thee; for I _____
　　　　_____
　　　　_____ ."

2

31.   Romans 6:23, "For the wages of sin is death; but the gift of

_____

_____ ."

32.   John 1:12, "But as many as received him, to them gave he power to _____

_____

_____ ."

NOTES

Other facts about science such as the value of snowfall and the importance of lightning in the rainfall are taught by Job (Job 38:22-26). Only with the most modern instruments have scientists proved the truth of these facts.

Scientists have studied many years to find that plants and animals bear only their own kind. For example, dogs will only bear dogs, and cats will only bear cats. This fact was written in the Bible (Genesis 1:24) long ago.

Much information is being found today about the Flood in the time of Noah. Scientists have uncovered much to prove that the earth had a great flood (Genesis, Chapter 7).

The city of Jericho has been uncovered. Men have found that the walls of that city did fall outward. They also have found that the city was burned. They have found one part of the wall that did not fall. Reread the story of Rahab (Joshua 6:20 through 24).

How could the Bible writers know all these things? God told them what to write. God knows everything!

People laughed at Noah when he built the ark.

Circle the words that tell some of the things God made.

2.21

land	stars	water	sun	trees	grass
moon	birds	light	man	fish	

```
F  W  A  T  E  R  A  T
I  J  G  F  D  E  U  R
S  L  I  G  H  T  B  E
H  K  W  E  V  C  T  E
M  B  I  R  D  S  X  S
O  L  G  R  A  S  S  R
L  M  I  H  N  P  Q  C
A  O  S  D  S  M  A  N
N  O  U  Z  F  A  Y  B
D  N  N  S  T  A  R  S
```

 Finish these statements. Here are some facts the Bible told about before scientists knew about them.

2.22   The earth was _____ .

2.23   The "springs of the _____ ."

2.24   The value of _____ .

2.25   Plants and animals bear their own _____ .

2.26   Noah's _____ happened.

Answer this question.

2.27   How did the Bible writers know about these things before scientists? _____

_____

_____

Read James 1:18.

Your body. After God made the universe and the world, the Bible says God took dust from the ground and formed it into a man. God then breathed into him and gave him life.

Scientists have found that the sixteen **elements** which are in the human body are found in the dust of the earth also.

The greatest wonder of all the wonders that God has created is the human body. The human body was carefully planned by God. Think about a few of your body's wonders.

Your eyes are wonderful! Your eyes can see color, shape, size, and distance. Over one hundred muscles and over 100 million nerves are in the eye (add 6 zeros after 100). The human eye is far more wonderful than any camera that man can make.

God made the outer ear like a shell to catch sound. The inside of the ear is much like a grand piano. God is a master **craftsman**.

God made your nose to do several things. As you breathe through your nose, it warms the air for your lungs. It keeps dirt and small objects out of your lungs. Your nose is also made to smell things.

Your bones are more than a rack on which to hang your body. Each bone is made in a special way for a special purpose. Your bones grow as your body grows. No builder today could make anything like a human bone.

Your skin is an amazing thing. Think how is stretches to cover your body as you grow. The skin on your fingers is special. In all the world, no two people have the same fingerprints.

Scientists say that you have about 300,000 hairs. Jesus said (Matthew 10:30), "But the very hairs of your head are all numbered." God knows everything about you.

More than 600 muscles are in your body. These muscles help you to make all kinds of movements.

Your lungs work without you thinking about them. Even when you are sleeping, your lungs are working. Suppose you had to think each time you needed a breath.

The blood has over 1,000 jobs to do. The blood never stops flowing, but is pushed by the heart pump, which is a masterpiece. The heart pushes seven tons of blood every day. Not long ago scientists realized the value of the body's blood. Moses wrote (Leviticus 17:11), "the life of the flesh is in the blood."

God has made the body with the ability to repair itself. When the body is hurt, first you have a sore, then a scab, and then new skin forms. Can you imagine a car that could repair itself?

One of the best things of all about your body is your brain and your ability to talk.

Scientists have tried for hundreds of years to make a human body, but only God can make life. Scientists have been able to make some **artificial** body parts, but they are only copies of the ones God has made.

God exists. He made the universe, the world, and the people. God made each person in a special way. God is a great, wise, and powerful God. Your body is proof that God exists.

Write at least one thing you know about each of these parts of your body.

2.28 Eyes

_____

_____

_____

_____

2.32 Heart

_____

_____

_____

_____

WHAT DO YOU KNOW ABOUT YOUR BODY?

2.33 Lungs

_____

_____

_____

_____

2.29 Bones

_____

_____

_____

_____

2.34 Nose

_____

_____

_____

_____

2.30 Skin

_____

_____

_____

_____

2.35 Ears

_____

_____

_____

_____

2.31 Muscles

_____

_____

_____

_____

2.36 Blood

_____

_____

_____

_____

Learn these two verses. Say them to your teacher.

2.37

"Know ye that the Lord he is God: it is he that hath made us and not we ourselves; we are his people, and the sheep of his pasture." (Psalm 100:3) "I will praise thee; for I am fearfully and wonderfully made: marvellous are thy works; and that my soul knoweth right well." (Psalm 139:14)

Teacher check _____

                        Initial   Date

Complete this activity.

2.38

Find a stamp pad. Ask permission for two or three friends to make their fingerprints on your paper. Compare them. Then make the fingerprints into a picture.

 **Write the letter of the correct word to finish the sentence.**

2.39 _____ Jesus' Father is __ .
2.40 _____ Jesus came to earth from __ .
2.41 _____ The father of the Jewish nation is __ .
2.42 _____ The one who died for our sins was __ .

a. heaven
b. Abraham
c. Sarah
d. Jesus
e. God

 Review the material in this section to prepare for the Self Test. The Self Test will check your understanding of this section. Any items you miss on this test will show you what areas you need to restudy.

SELF TEST 2

Complete these verses (each answer, 4 points).

2.01   Psalm 100:3 "Know ye that the Lord he is a. _____ :
it is he that hath b. _____ us and not we
ourselves; we are his c. _____ , and the
sheep of his pasture."

2.02   Psalm 139:14 "I will a. _____ thee; for I am
fearfully and wonderfully b. _____ :
marvellous are thy c. _____ ; and that my
soul knoweth right well."

Complete these sentences (each answer, 4 points).

2.03   God promised Abraham many _____ .

2.04   God promised the Jewish people a _____ .

2.05   God said, "I will be your God and ye shall be my _____
_____ ."

2.06   God said that He would punish those who hurt the _____
_____ .

2.07   Before Jesus came to earth, He was in _____ .

Answer *true* **or** *false* (each answer, 2 points).

2.08   _____ Jesus took the punishment for our sins.

2.09   _____ Thomas Aquinas wrote laws to prove that God exists.

2.010   _____ Plants and animals sometimes do not bear their own kind.

2.011   _____ The greatest wonder that God created is your body.

2.012   _____ Life is in the bones.

Write the letter of the correct answer (each answer, 3 points).

2.013   God made man from _____ .
         a. dry bones   b. dust

2.014   The greatest wonder of all creation is _____ .
         a. man's body   b. stars

2.015   Man cannot make _____ .
         a. a camera   b. an eye

2.016   Our bodies have about _____ muscles.
         a. 600   b. 300,000

2.017   The heart pushes about _____ tons of blood each day.
         a. seven   b. three

2.018   "The life of the flesh is in the _____ ."
         a. brain   b. blood

2.019   Only _____ can make life.
         a. scientists   b. God

2.020   The Bible says the earth is _____ .
         a. flat   b. round

2.021   The universe was begun by _____ .
         a. God   b. a tiny thing

2.022   Jesus' Father is _____ .
         a. God   b. Abraham

2.023   Abraham's son was _____ .
         a. Ur   b. Isaac

2.024   A friar is _____ .
         a. a cooking pan   b. a member of a
                                            religious group

Answer these questions (each numbered answer, 5 points).

2.025   How can you know that God exists? _____
         _____

2.026   What are two facts about Thomas Aquinas?
         a. _____

         _____

         b. _____

         _____

	Possible Score	100
	My Score	_____
	Teacher check	_____
		Initial Date

24

III. MAN'S NEED OF GOD

People need to know many things. They need to know how to read and to write. They need to know mathematics and spelling. People need to know how to take care of themselves. Something much more important than any of these things is needed, however. Can you think what it might be?

In this section you will read about man's most important need—the need to know God. You will also learn how you can know God.

☐ **Review these objectives.**

5. To explain why man needs God,
6. To tell how man can know God, and
7. To recite four Bible verses.

☐ **Restudy this word.**
worship

 Read Second Corinthians 4:3 through 7.

MAN AND RELIGION

Most people have a religion. Hundreds of different religions are taught in the world. Why do you think so many religions exist?

The need for worship. All over the world people are **worshiping** gods. In some countries people think that several gods exist. Some people think four gods exist. Some think hundreds of gods exist.

In some places people worship wicked spirits or dead relatives. Some people believe that their gods will hurt them or do bad things to them if they do wrong.

In some parts of the world, people worship gods made of wood or of stone. Some people believe that the sun and moon are gods. They bow down and pray to them. They ask the sun and moon to take care of them and to help them.

Can the sun or the moon help people? No, neither the sun nor the moon have life. They are not persons with power to help others.

Some boys and girls, and adults too, carry lucky charms, rabbits' feet, and medals. These people think these things will keep them safe.

The need for God. Why do people worship things? People worship things because all men are born with a deep need for a god to worship. If they do not know about the true God, then they will make up other gods. They will worship the things God made instead of God Himself.

Many men and women, boys and girls will not hear about the true God unless the people who do know Him tell them. Maybe you will tell others

25

about the true God.

All of these people are not across an ocean or hundreds of miles away. Some people near you do not know who God is. They are worshiping other things because they have a deep need for God, but they do not know how to find Him.

Satan is "the god of this world." The Bible says (Second Corinthians 4:4) he has "... blinded minds of them which believe not...."

 Tell about some ways people worship when they do not know the true God.

3.1 _____
_____
_____
_____

 **Circle** *yes* **or** *no*.

3.2	Do some people worship wicked spirits?	yes	no
3.3	Do all men have a need to worship God?	yes	no
3.4	Do some men make up gods?	yes	no
3.5	Does everyone in our country know the true God?	yes	no
3.6	Would you like to tell someone about God?	yes	no

 Study this chart.

Fact—known to be true
Fiction—imagined, not true
Opinion—what someone thinks or believes

Read what these people are saying. Underline the fact in blue, fiction in green, and opinion in red.

3.7 The Bible says, "In the beginning God created the heaven and the earth."

3.8 Once there was a tiny thing that grew until it became the earth.

3.9 I think the universe just happened.

3.10 I believe Jesus was a good man but not a Saviour.

3.11 Once upon a time there was a little chick, named Chicken Little.

3.12 Jesus said, "I am the way, the truth, and the life."

Read Second Timothy 3:14 through 17.

GOD AND MAN

The universe, the earth, and our bodies all tell of God. The Bible tells the most about God.

God has had a plan for you since the beginning when He created the universe. To know His plan for you, you must read God's Word, the Bible.

God's Word. God wants to talk to you. Today God does not appear to people personally. He has a way that He talks to people. God gave people a long letter to read. God's letter is the Bible. The Bible tells many things about God and about His work. The Bible tells about man and what man should do.

God did not write the letter with a pencil or pen. God chose forty men who loved Him to write the Bible. He guided them so that what they wrote was exactly what He wanted to have written. Sometimes God would give the writer a dream. Often God made him see pictures of things that were going to happen. Then the writer would write these things down.

How would you feel if you wrote a letter to someone and they did not read it? You would be sad. Imagine how God feels if you do not read His letter. Reading the Bible is very important.

Complete this activity.

3.13   Choose ten books of the Bible and find out who wrote the ten books. Find out something about each man and learn the message of each Bible book in your study. Write your findings on another piece of paper. Have your teacher check your work.

Teacher check _____

Initial   Date

Answer these questions.

3.14 How can we know about God? _____

_____

_____

3.15 How does God talk to you? _____

_____

3.16 Why should you read the Bible? _____

_____

3.17 How many men did God use to write the Bible? _____

_____

3.18 Tell three facts of science found in the Bible (review Section II).

a. _____

_____

b. _____

_____

c. _____

_____

God's plan. God's plan was to send His Son to die for your sins. God prepared a body for His Son so that He could be like us. Jesus was born, lived on earth, died, and rose again.

Did God punish Jesus because of His own sins? No, Jesus had no sin. Jesus came to die for your sins. Jesus came to be your Saviour from sin. Now you may want to ask Jesus to be your Saviour. You can talk to God in prayer. Say something like this:

"Dear Lord, I have sinned. Thank you for sending Jesus to die for my sin. I cannot help myself, but You can save me. Please come into my life and make me part of your family. Thank you. Amen."

If you have already asked Jesus to be your Saviour, maybe you could tell someone else how to do it.

Learn these verses. Say them from memory to your teacher.

3.19 Romans 6:23. "For the wages of sin is death; but the gift of God is eternal life through Jesus Christ our Lord."

3.20 John 1:12. "But as many as received him, to them gave he power to become the sons of God, even to them that believe on his name."

Write the correct word from the list to complete the sentence.

Son   sin   died

us   God

3.21   God sent Jesus, His only _____ , to earth.

3.22   Jesus _____ for our sins.

3.23   Jesus had no _____ of His own.

3.24   All men need _____ .

Answer *true* **or** *false.*

3.25   _____ All religions are good.

3.26   _____ Everyone in our country knows the true God.

3.27   _____ Some men worship the things God made, instead of worshiping God.

3.28   _____ We need blood to live.

3.29   _____ God is Jesus' Father.

3.30   _____ Before Jesus came to earth, He was in heaven.

3.31   _____ God guided the Bible writers as they wrote the Bible.

Finish these verses.

3.32   Psalm 100:3, "Know ye that the Lord _____

_____

_____ ."

3.33   Psalm 139:14, "I will praise thee; for I _____

_____

_____ ."

3.34   Romans 6:23, "For the wages of sin is death; but the gift of
        God is _____

_____ ."

3.35   John 1:12, "But as many as received him, to them gave he
        power to become the _____

_____ ."

Before you take this last Self Test, you may want to do one or more of these self checks.

1. _____   Read the objectives. See if you can do them.
2. _____   Restudy the material related to any objectives that you cannot do.
3. _____   Use the SQ3R study procedure to review the material:
        a.   **S**can the sections,
        b.   **Q**uestion yourself,
        c.   **R**ead to answer your questions,
        d.   **R**ecite the answers to yourself, and
        e.   **R**eview areas you did not understand.
4. _____   Review all vocabulary, activities, and Self Tests, writing a correct answer for every wrong answer.

SELF TEST 3

Write the correct word from the list in each blank (each answer, 3 points).

Lord	sins	body
name	fact	Bible
forty	heaven	Jesus
ten	hell	friar

3.01   Jesus came to earth to die for our _____ .

3.02   God's Son is _____ .

3.03   Before Jesus came to earth, He was in _____ .

3.04   The greatest wonder of all that God created is the

_____ .

3.05   God talks to us through the _____ .

3.06   God used _____ men to write the Bible.

3.07   Romans 6:23, "For the wages of sin is death; but the gift of God is eternal life through Jesus Christ our _____ ."

3.08   John 1:12, "But as many as received him, to them gave he power to become the sons of God, even to them that believe on his _____ ."

3.09   A name for a member of a certain religious group is a

_____ .

3.010   Something known to be true is a _____ .

Answer *true* **or** *false* (each answer, 2 points).

3.011 _____ People deserve to be punished for their sins.

3.012 _____ Jesus died for our sins.

3.013 _____ God promised the Jews a Saviour.

3.014 _____ God said He would punish those who hurt the Jews.

3.015 _____ The Bible writers wrote what they wanted to.

3.016 _____ We can know about God because of what He does.

3.017 _____ All men do not need God.

3.018 _____ We can see the wind.

31

3.019 _____ Abraham did not have any children.
3.020 _____ Sarah was Abraham's wife.
3.021 _____ Jesus never sinned.

Write the letter of the correct answer on the blank (each answer, 3 points).

3.022   Abraham's name means _____ .
             a. princess   c. Saviour
             b. father of a nation

3.023   God gave Abraham and his family the land of _____ .
             a. Canaan   c. Ur
             b. United States

3.024   Thomas Aquinas wanted to be a _____ .
             a. farmer   c. friar
             b. soldier

3.025   Psalm 100:3, "Know ye that the Lord he is _____ ."
             a. good   c. great
             b. God

3.026   God promised Abraham _____ .
             a. houses   c. children
             b. good times

3.027   Psalm 139:14, "I will praise thee; for I am fearfully and _____ made."
             a. awfully   c. wonderfully
             b. greatly

3.028   Life is in the _____ .
             a. blood   c. muscles
             b. brain

3.029   Thomas Aquinas wrote _____ to prove that God exists.
             a. poems   c. laws
             b. hymns

3.030   God said, "I will be your God and you will be my _____ ."
             a. slaves   c. people
             b. servants

3.031   The Bible is _____ .
             a. a science book   c. a law book
             b. God's Word

3.032   All men have a deep need to _____ .
          a. know God   c. have a garden
          b. have a puppy

Answer these questions (each numbered answer, 5 points).
3.033   What are three facts about science found in the Bible?
          a. _____
          b. _____
          c. _____
3.034   Why did Jesus come to earth? _____
          _____
3.035   Why should you read the Bible? _____
          _____
          _____

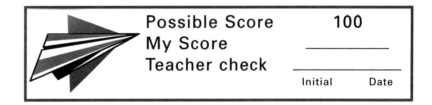

	Possible Score	100
My Score	
Teacher check	
	Initial	Date

  Before taking the LIFEPAC Test, you may want to do one or more of these self checks.

1. _____   Read the objectives. See if you can do them.
2. _____   Restudy the material related to any objectives that you cannot do.
3. _____   Use the SQ3R study procedure to review the material.
4. _____   Review activities, Self Tests, and LIFEPAC vocabulary words.
5. _____   Restudy areas of weakness indicated by the last Self Test.